Deck Officer Study Guide

*Preparation for the United States Coast Guard
Merchant Marine License Examinations*

VOLUME 6
DECK EXAMINATION ILLUSTRATION BOOK

Edited by:

CAPTAIN JOSEPH S. MURPHY, II
Professor, Department of Marine Transportation
Massachusetts Maritime Academy

Academy Publishing Company
6 Munroe Parkway
Wareham, MA 02571

COMMANDANT PUBLICATION P16721.6A IS NO LONGER IN PRINT.

Color diagrams are no longer used for deck examination modules. Black and white illustrations or diagrams are now printed in the rear of deck examination booklets when they are required to answer a question.

ISBN 1-881349-07-9 (Volume 6)
ISBN 1-881349-02-0 (6 Volume Set)
Printed in the United States

US. DEPARTMENT OF
TRANSPORTATION

UNITED STATES
COAST GUARD

Commandant (G-MVP)
United States Coast Guard

Mailing Address:

2100 SECOND STREET SW
WASHINGTON, DC 20593-0001
(202) 267-2705

9 JAN 1992
COMDTPUB P16721.6A

COMMANDANT PUBLICATION P16721.6A

Subj: Merchant Marine Deck Examination Illustration Book

1.   PURPOSE

This publication contains illustrations needed by an applicant during an examination for a merchant marine deck license or endorsement on a merchant mariner's document.

2.   DISCUSSION

a.   Applicants testing for merchant marine deck licenses and merchant mariner's document endorsements may have to answer questions that refer to an illustration or diagram. This publication contains the illustrations needed.

b.   The Coast Guard uses a computerized random generation system for creating examination modules. To streamline the process of creating module test booklets, the illustrations needed to answer exam questions have been incorporated in examination illustration books. This allows applicants to view both the exam question and the illustration it may refer to at the same time.

c.   The January 1992 edition of this publication contains all illustrations required by questions in the question bank as of January 1992.

3.   PROCEDURE

a.   This publication is effective upon receipt. It supersedes the September 1988 edition. Regional Examination Centers (RECs) shall destroy the covers of the September 1988 edition and discard the remainder of each book.

3. b. RECs will make this publication available to applicants testing with a deck merchant marine examination. Applicants who have purchased copies of this publication from the Government Printing Office (GPO) may not use their personal copies. Each REC is to allow only the REC copies of this publication to be used in the exam room. The covers of this publication held by the RECs will be pecan; the covers of this publication available to the public through GPO will be yellow.

4. ORDERING INFORMATION

    a. RECs will be provided with an initial supply of this publication. Replacement and additional copies are available from Commandant (G-MVP-5), FTS 267-2705, Commercial (202) 267-2705.

    b. The public and other Coast Guard units may order copies of this publication from the GPO at the following address:

    Superintendent of Documents
    U.S. Government Printing Office
    Washington, CD 20402

    This book may also be ordered by telephone and charged to a national credit card by calling (202) 783-3238.

    A. E. Henn
    Rear Admiral, United States Coast Guard
    Chief, Office of Marine Safety, Security
    and Environmental Protection

Non-Standard Distribution:

C:e   Toledo (350); Boston, Miami (225); New Orleans (150); Baltimore, San Francisco, Honolulu (125); Charleston, San Juan, Long Beach, Anchorage, Houston (75); Portland, Memphis, St. Louis, Puget Sound (50); Juneau, Norfolk, Guam, Ketchikan (25) (only).

C: m   New York (250) (only).

COMMANDANT PUBLICATION P16721.6A IS NO LONGER IN PRINT.

Color diagrams are no longer used for deck examination modules. Black and white illustrations or diagrams are now printed in the rear of deck examination booklets when they are required to answer a question.

MERCHANT MARINE DECK EXAMINATION ILLUSTRATION BOOK

TABLE OF CONTENTS

INSTRUCTIONS

1. Some of the questions in the deck examination booklets require the use of an illustration or diagram to answer the question. All of these illustrations and diagrams are contained in this publication.

2. If a question requires the use of an illustration or diagram, it will be specifically stated in the lead-in sentence, or stem, of the question. For example, if the question in your examination booklet is, "Which of the symbols in illustration D018NG represents a warm front?" you must find illustration D018NG in this book in order to answer the question.

3. The illustrations in this publication are divided into chapters based on the two letter abbreviation at the end of the illustration number. The abbreviations indicate the general area from which the illustration was taken and are listed below. The Rules of the Road diagrams are contained in the first chapter and are identified by numbers only.

    DG - Deck General
    NG - Navigation General
    SA - Safety
    SL - Sail

4. Some illustration numbers have been reserved in this publication for continuity purposes and for future use. The illustrations formerly associated with these numbers have been either cancelled or incorporated into the Stability Data Reference Book (COMDTPUB P16721.31).

5. Applicants taking an examination who wish to make a comment or protest concerning any illustration or diagram in this publication should complete a Comment/Protest form for the question involved and give it to the examiner.

6. Individuals not taking an examination who wish to make a comment on any illustration or diagram in this publication should send a written comment, citing this publication and each illustration or diagram commented on, to:

    Commandant (G-MVP-5)
    United States Coast Guard
    DECK ILLUSTRATION COMMENT
    2100 Second Street, S.W.
    Washington, D.C. 20593-0001

All written comments submitted by the general public will be reviewed prior to revising this publication. All comments are welcomed and written comments will receive a letter or postcard indicating that they were received. Valid comments will be incorporated into this publication.

CHAPTER 1
RULES OF THE ROAD

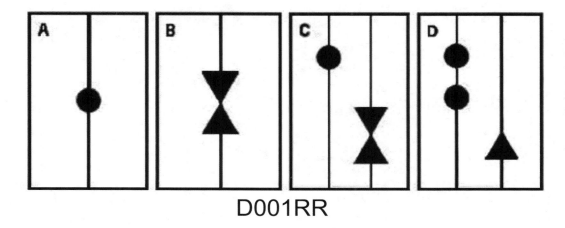

D001RR

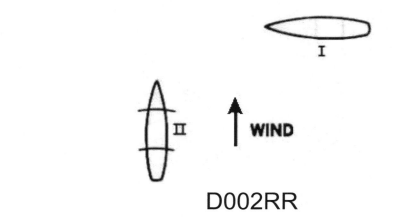

D002RR

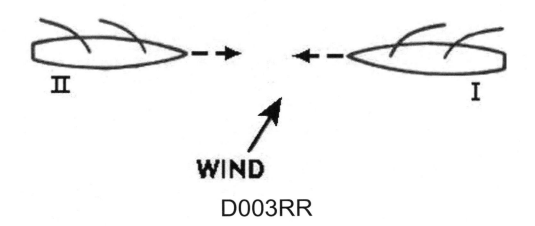

D003RR

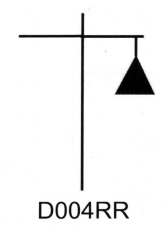

D004RR

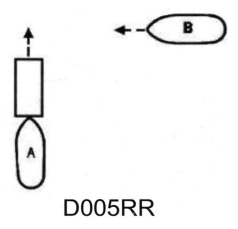

D005RR

D006RR

D007RR

D008RR

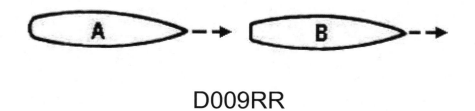

D009RR

D010RR

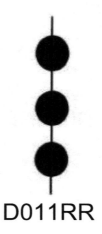

D011RR

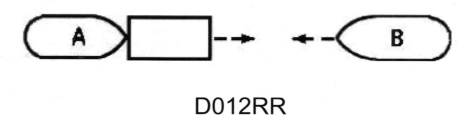

D012RR

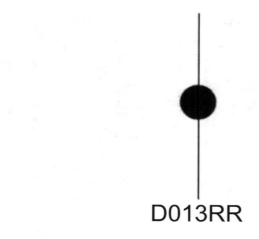

D013RR

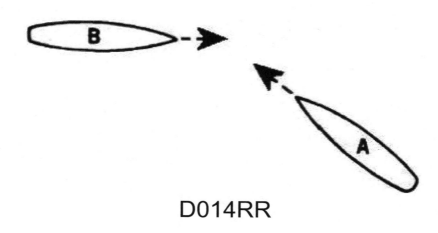

D014RR

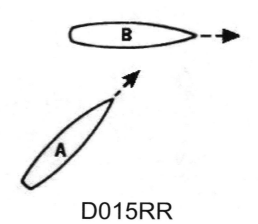

D015RR

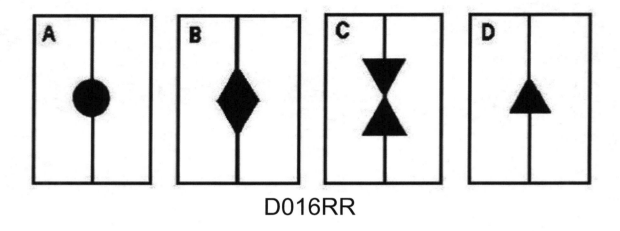

D016RR

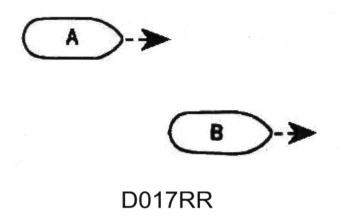

D017RR

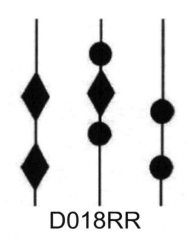

D018RR

BASKET

D019RR

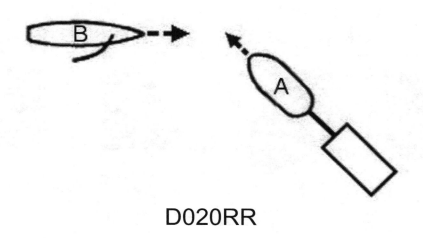

D020RR

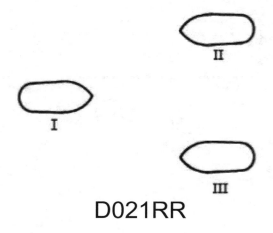

D021RR

D022RR

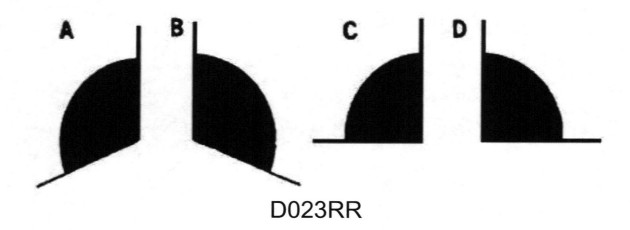

D023RR

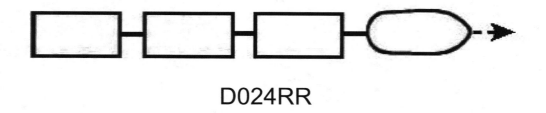

D024RR

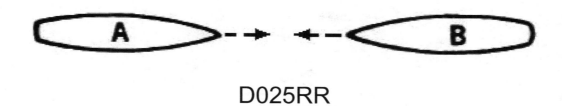

D025RR

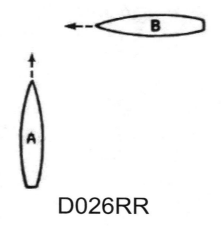

D026RR

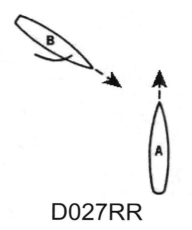

D027RR

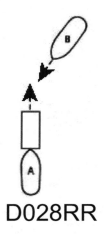

D028RR

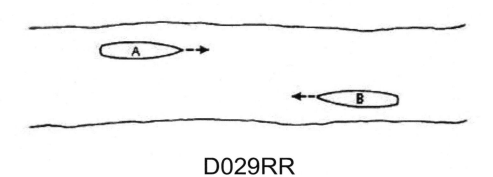

D029RR

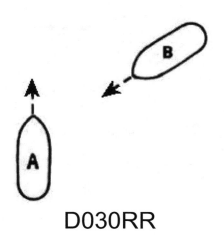

D030RR

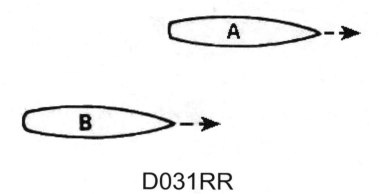

D031RR

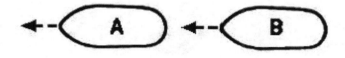

D032RR

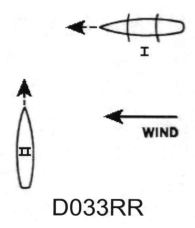

D033RR

D034RR

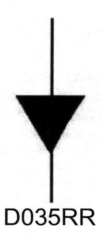

D035RR

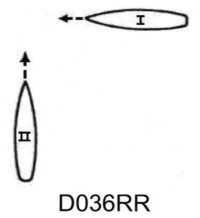

D036RR

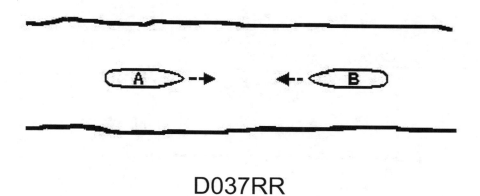

D037RR

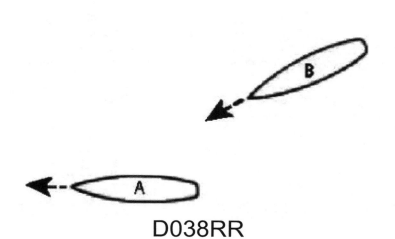

D038RR

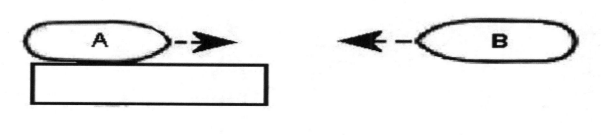

D039RR

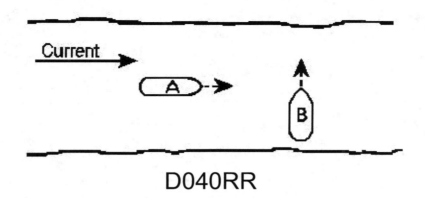

D040RR

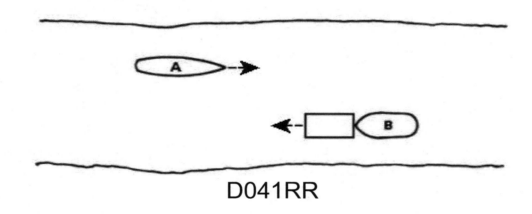

D041RR

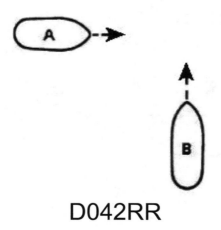

D042RR

D043RR

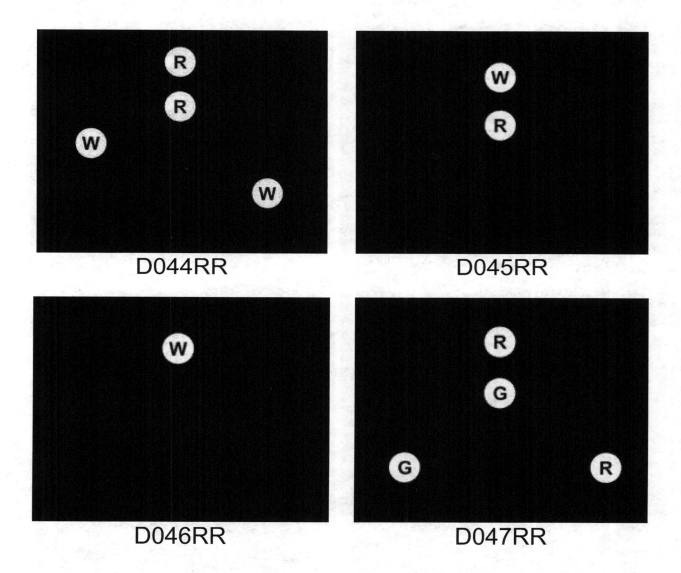

D044RR   D045RR

D046RR   D047RR

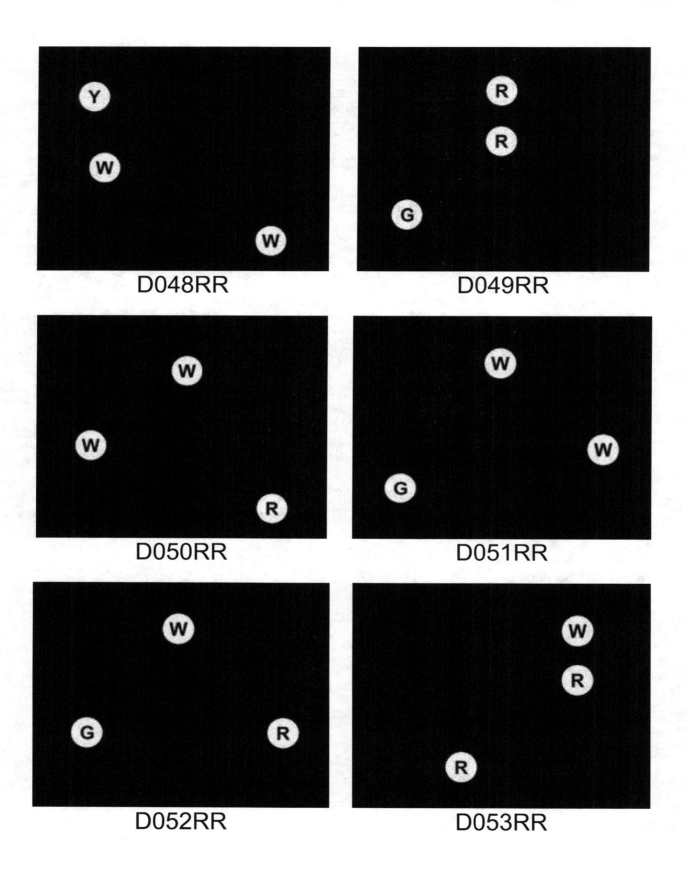

D048RR

D049RR

D050RR

D051RR

D052RR

D053RR

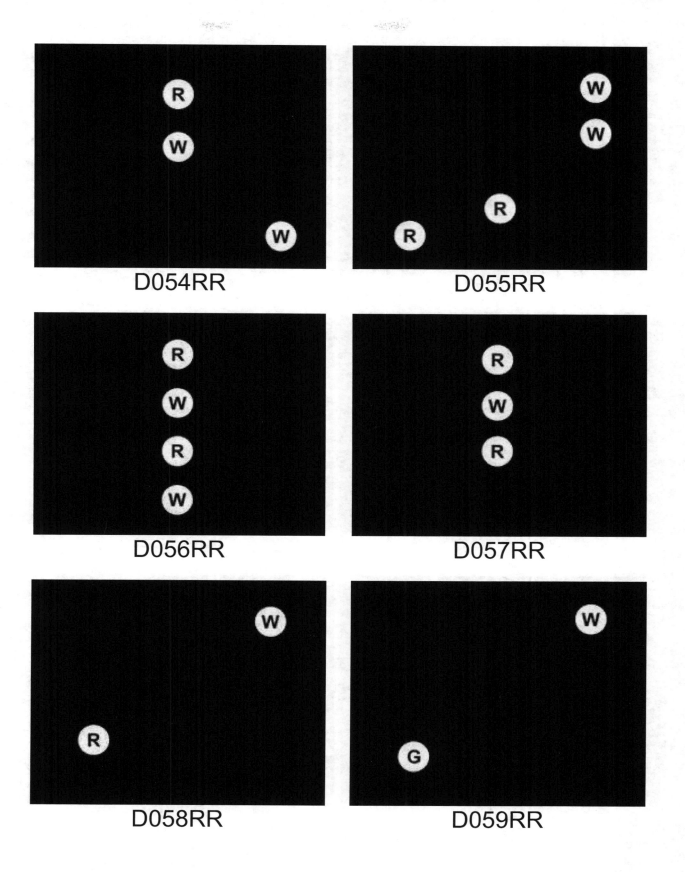

D054RR

D055RR

D056RR

D057RR

D058RR

D059RR

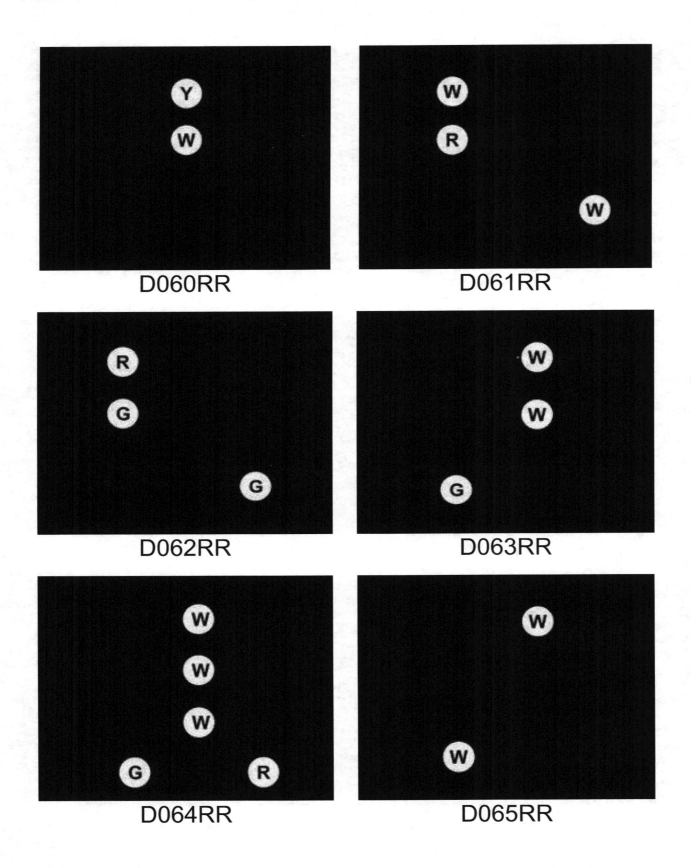

D060RR

D061RR

D062RR

D063RR

D064RR

D065RR

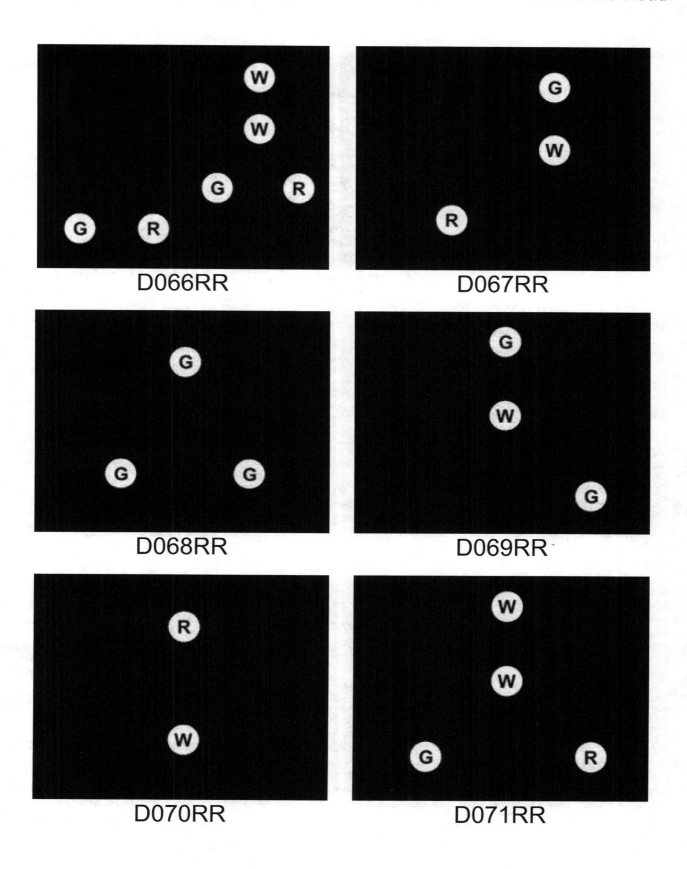

D066RR

D067RR

D068RR

D069RR

D070RR

D071RR

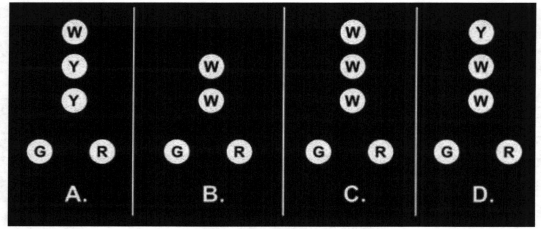

D072RR

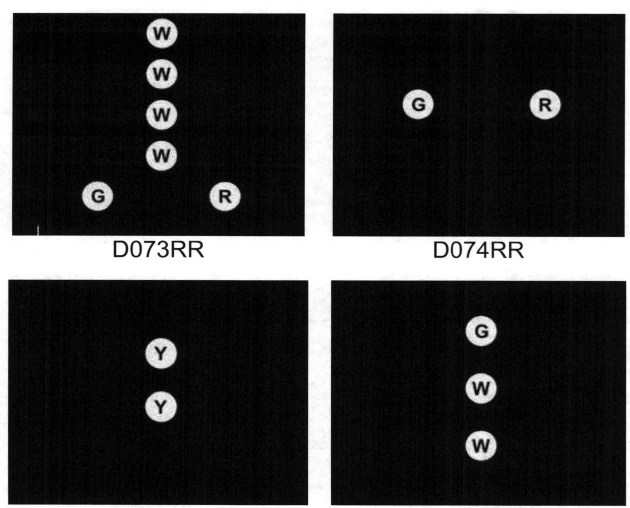

D073RR

D074RR

D075RR

D076RR

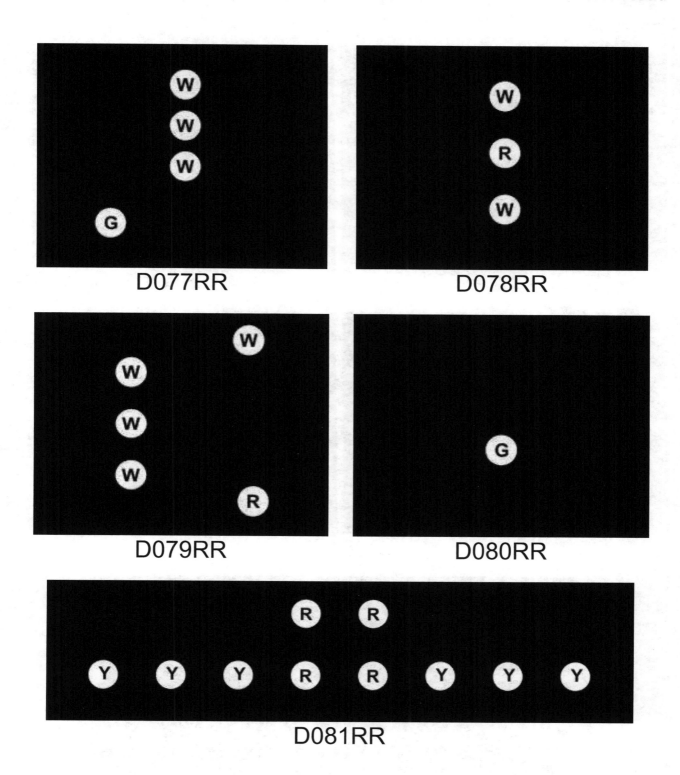

D077RR

D078RR

D079RR

D080RR

D081RR

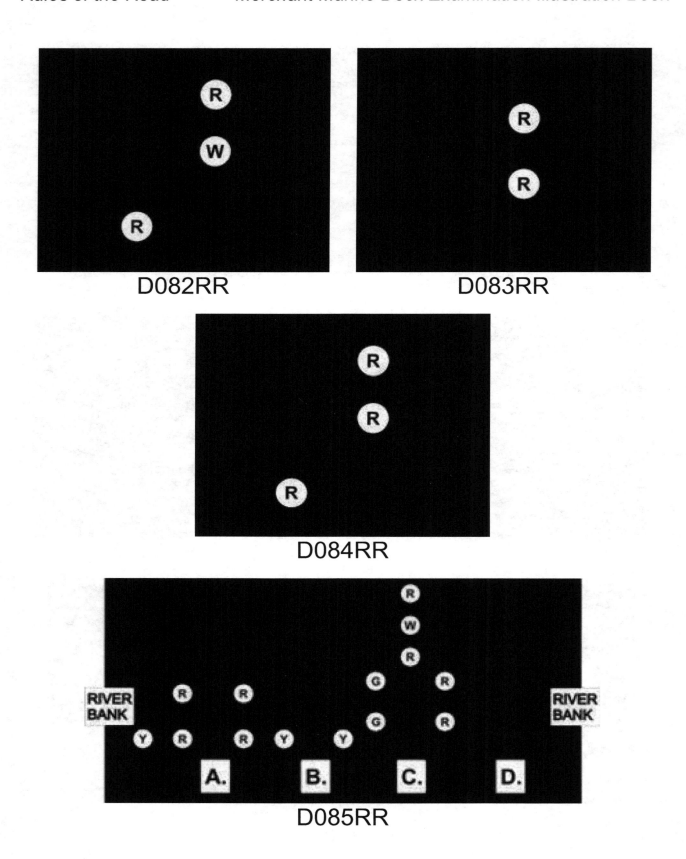

D082RR

D083RR

D084RR

D085RR

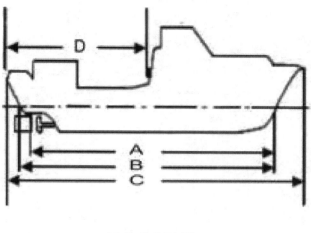

D086RR

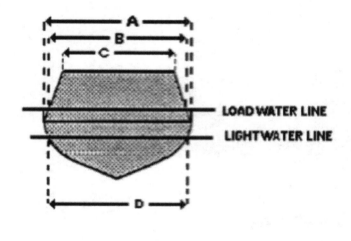

D087RR

CHAPTER 2
DECK GENERAL

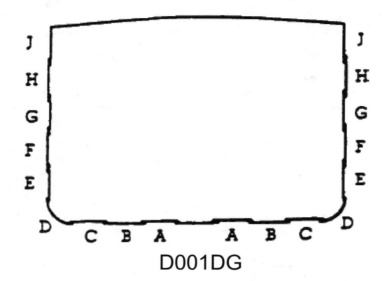

D001DG

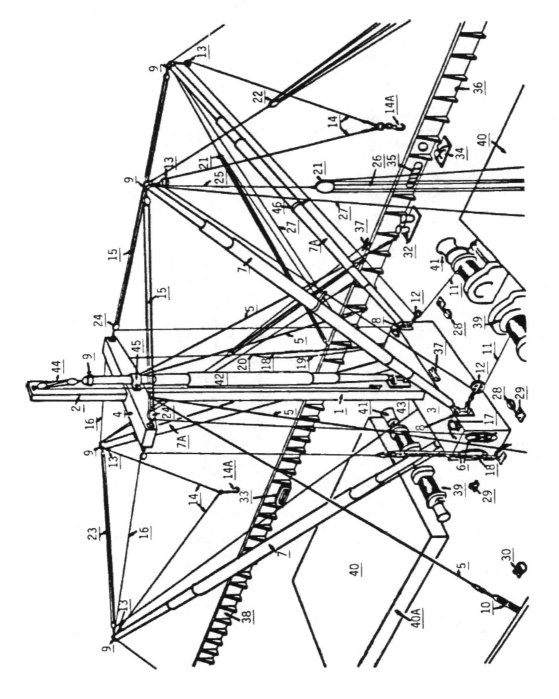

D002DG

DELETED

A

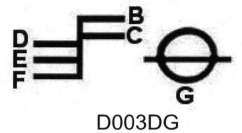

D003DG

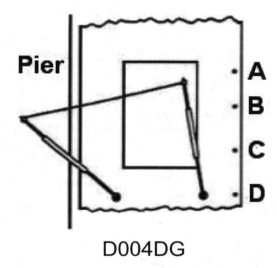

D004DG

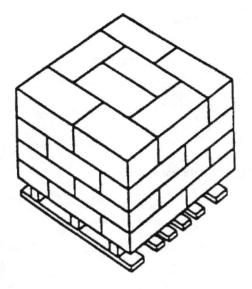

D005DG

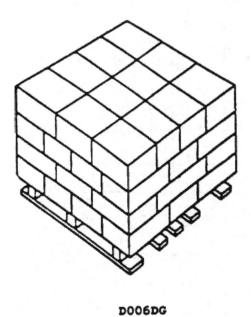

D006DG

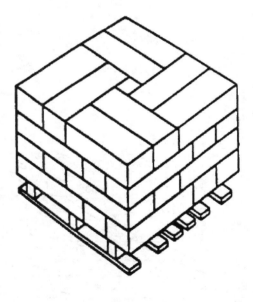

D007DG

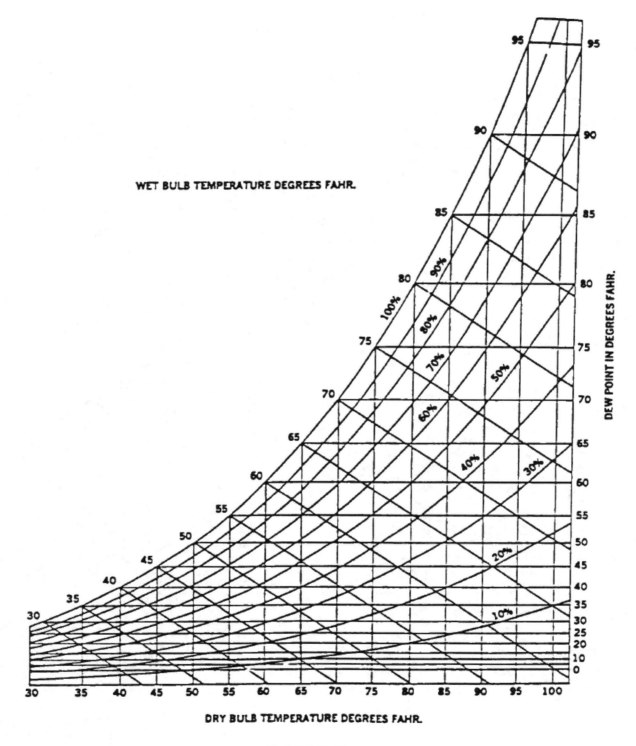

WET BULB TEMPERATURE DEGREES FAHR.

DEW POINT IN DEGREES FAHR.

DRY BULB TEMPERATURE DEGREES FAHR.

D008DG

D009DG THROUGH D018DG RESERVED

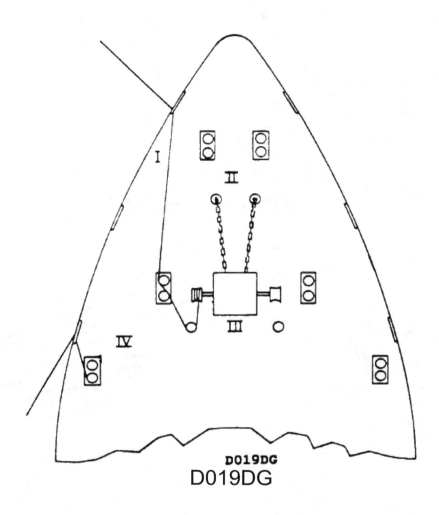

D019DG

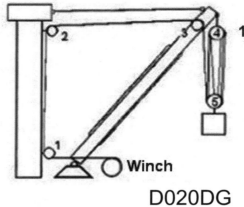

1, 2, 3 - Single sheave
          fairlead blocks

4, 5 - Triple sheave
          blocks

D020DG

D021DG RESERVED

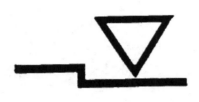

D022DG   D023DG

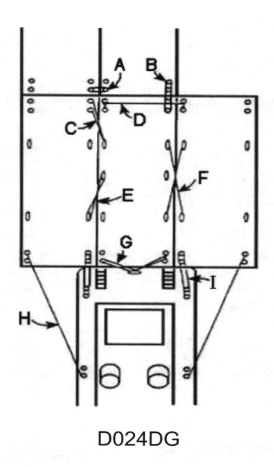

D024DG

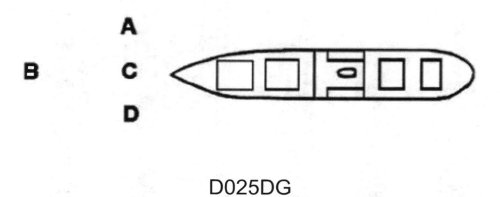

D025DG

D026DG THROUGH D028DG RESERVED

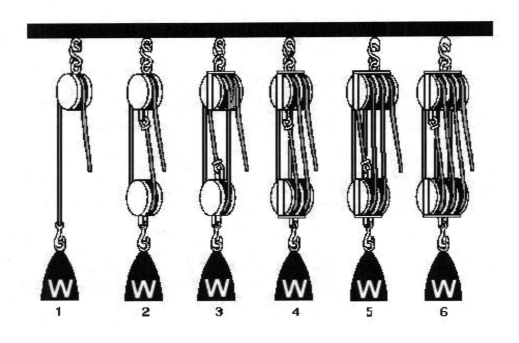

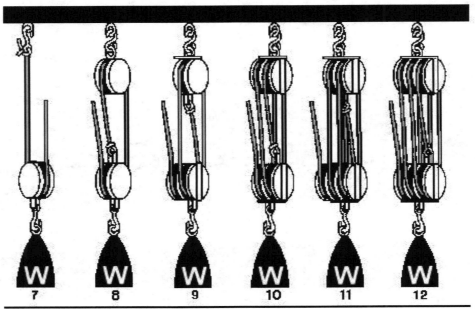

D029DG

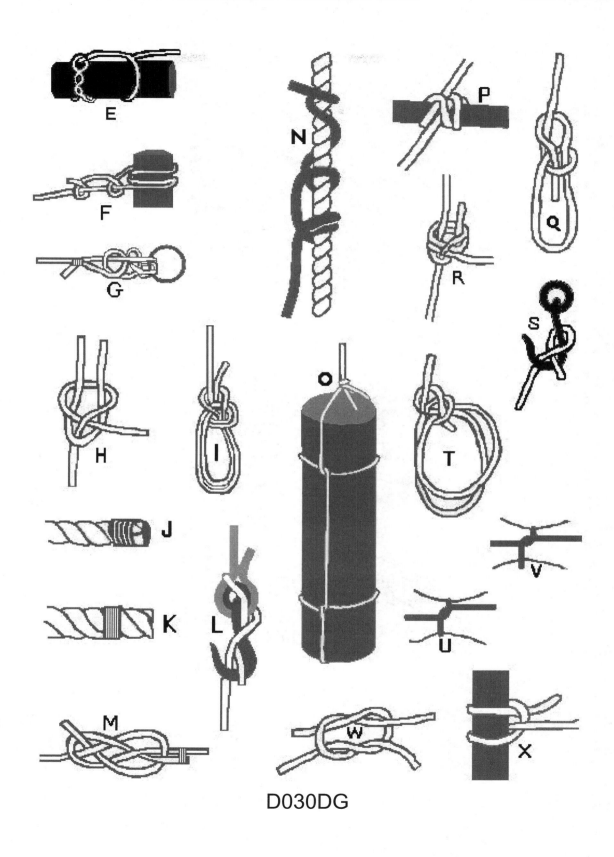

D030DG

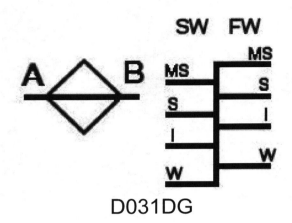

D031DG

12   12
11   11
10   10
9   9
8   8
7   7
AFT DRAFT   FWD DRAFT
MARKS   MARKS

D032DG

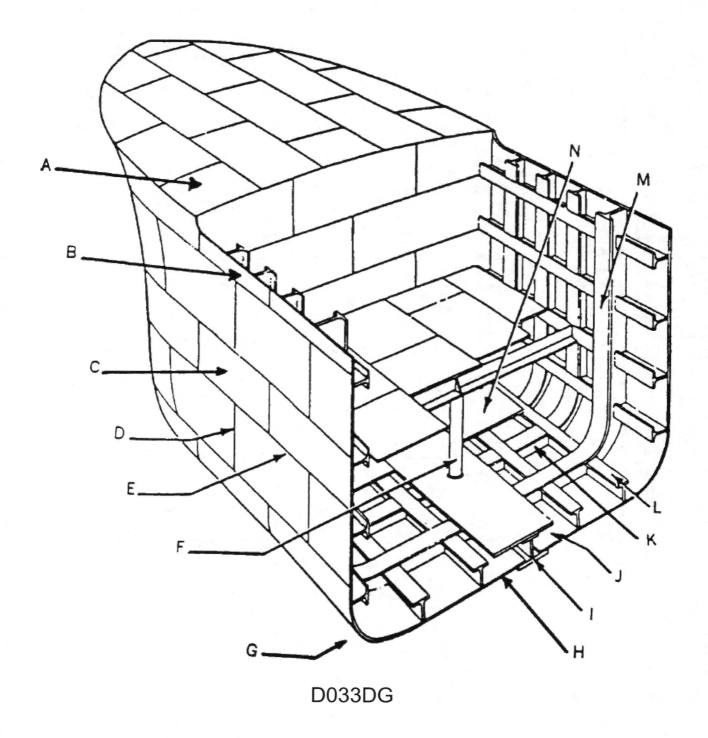

D033DG

HEADING (TRUE)	BEARING (TRUE)	RANGE (YDS)	REMARKS
228°			INITIAL HEADING
228°	232°	2260	ON INITIAL COURSE
228°	234°	1700	RIGHT FULL RUDDER ORDERE
230°	236°	1490	
252°	235°	1275	
275°	231°	1000	
316°	214°	850	
352°	198°	975	
022°	194°	1210	
053°	197°	1430	
087°	202°	1600	
115°	209°	1690	
151°	217°	1700	
183°	225°	1600	
218°	232°	1350	RUDDER AMIDSHIPS
228°	235°	1125	STEADY ON 228°

D034DG

HEADING (TRUE)	BEARING (TRUE)	RANGE (YDS)	REMARKS
333°			INITIAL HEADING
333°	315°	2125	ON INITIAL COURSE
333°	310°	1650	LEFT FULL RUDDER ORDERED
327°	307°	1475	
310°	303°	1250	
278°	302°	1050	
268°	305°	900	
236°	318°	750	
196°	337°	800	
157°	344°	1100	
113°	340°	1350	
079°	332°	1525	
050°	324°	1575	
022°	318°	1550	
343°	308°	1400	RUDDER AMIDSHIPS
333°	302°	1175	STEADY ON 333°

D035DG

U.S. Department of Transportation

United States Coast Guard

Commandant
United States Coast Guard

Washington. D.C. 20593-0001
Staff Symbol.
Phone.

16710
8 Apr 87

Master, M/V HUDSON, O.N. 666666

Subj: M/V HUDSON
      Stability

Dear Sir:

A stability test, supervised by the U.S. Coast Guard, was conducted on the M/V HUDSON at San Diego, California on 08 April 1987. On the basis of this test, stability calculations have been performed. Results indicate that the stability of the M/V HUDSON, as presently outfitted and equipped, is satisfactory for operation in Ocean Service as indicated on the Certificate of Inspection, provided the following restrictions are strictly observed:

    1. a. The vessel shall only be loaded according to the instructions on the attached LOADING DIAGRAM bearing U.S. Coast Guard approval stamp dated 8 April 1986.

        b. Drilling fluids may be carried. The maximum specific gravity of the fluids shall not exceed 2.60.

        c. The vessel may engage in towing operations when loaded in accordance with the attached LOADING DIAGRAM.

    2. The height above the main deck of the center of gravity of the deck cargo shall not exceed the value shown on the LOADING DIAGRAM (3.0 feet). Such cargo must be positively secured against shifting prior to leaving protected waters.

    3. Permanent ballast, in the form of 64.4 long tons of high density fluids (sg. = 2.87), is to be maintained in the after peak tank. No permanent ballast shall be added, removed, altered and/or relocated without the authorization and supervision of the cognizant Officer in Charge, Marine Inspection.

    4. The maximum summer load line draft is 13 feet 8 3/8 inches. Trim shall be minimized and shall always result in a freeboard of at least 22 inches at the stern.

    5. No more than one centerline or P/S pair of the following tanks may be partially filled at any one time: fuel oil, lube oil, potable water, ballast/cargo water, fuel oil day tanks, drilling fluid. Cross-connections between all port and starboard tank pairs shall be kept closed at all times when underway.

D036DG

6. Main deck hatches and weather doors to the forecastle and machinery spaces shall be kept closed and fully secured at all times when underway, except when actually used for transit under safe conditions.

7. Main deck freeing ports shall be maintained operable and completely unobstructed at all times.

8. Bilges shall be kept pumped to minimum content at all times.

9. Suitable tables or curves for determining the capacities of full or partially full tanks shall be maintained aboard the vessel.

10. The Master should make every effort to determine the cause of any list of the vessel before taking corrective action.

It shall be the Master's responsibility to maintain the vessel in a satisfactory stability condition at all times.

This stability letter shall be posted under suitable transparent material in the pilothouse of the vessel so that all pages and the diagram are visible. It supersedes any stability information previously furnished the vessel.

Sincerely,

A. B. SEA
Lieutenant Commander
U.S. Coast Guard

Attachment: LOADING DIAGRAM for the subject vessel bearing U.S. Coast Guard approval stamp dated 8 April 1987

SEE NEXT PAGE FOR ATTACHMENT

D036DG continued

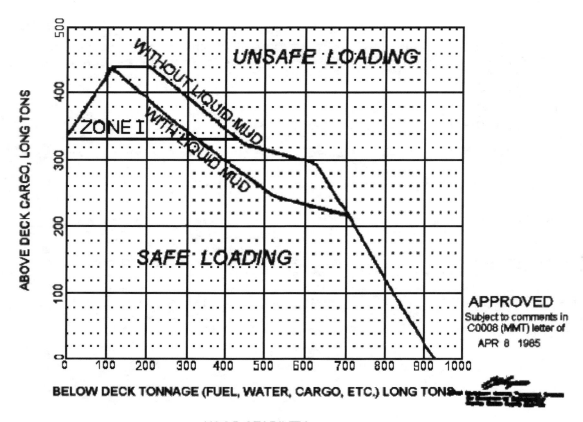

USCG STABILITY
LOADING INSTRUCTIONS

1. DRAW A VERTICAL LINE UP FROM 'BELOW DK' LOAD. DRAW HORIZONTAL LINE ACROSS FROM 'ABOVE DK' LOAD. IF THEY MEET BELOW THE CURVE THEN THE LOADING IS OK. IF THEY MEET ABOVE THE CURVE THEN YOU MUST CHANGE THE LOADING.

2. MAX. DECK CARGO VCG 3.00 FT. ABOVE DECK.

3. WHEN OPERATING IN ZONE 1 (I.E. MORE THAN 334 LONG TONS OF DECK CARGO) THE FOREPEAK BALLAST TANK SHALL BE PRESSED FULL.

D036DG continued

U.S. Department
of Transportation

**United States
Coast Guard**

Commandant
United States Coast Guard

Washington, D C 20593-0001
Staff Symbol
Phone

16710
13 May 87

Master, M/V SURVEYOR, O.N. 678678

Subj: M/V SURVEYOR
       Stability

Dear Sir:

A stability test, supervised by the U.S. Coast Guard, was conducted on
the M/V SURVEYOR at New Orleans, Louisiana, on 7 May 1987. On the
basis of this test, stability calculations have been performed.
Results indicate that the stability of the M/V SURVEYOR, as presently
outfitted and equipped, is satisfactory for operation in Ocean Service
as indicated on the Certificate of Inspection, provided the following
restrictions are strictly observed:

1. A maximum of 78 persons may be carried. In no case shall the
   number of persons exceed that allowed on the Certificate of
   Inspection.

2. The drafts as read on the draft marks shall not exceed 6 feet 3
   inches forward or 7 feet 1 inch aft. Trim should be minimized.
   A loadline is not authorized.

3. The height above the main deck of the center of gravity of deck
   cargo shall not exceed 2.0 feet. Such cargo must be positively
   secured before leaving protected waters.

4. A maximum of 50 long tons of deck cargo may be carried when no
   other below deck ballast or cargo is carried. When rig water
   is carried, a maximum of 35 long tons of deck cargo may be
   carried, and no other below deck cargo or ballast is permitted.

5. No permanent ballast or other such weights shall be added,
   removed, altered, and/or relocated without the authorization
   and supervision of the cognizant Officer in Charge, Marine
   Inspection.

6. No watertight bulkheads shall be removed or altered without the
   authorization and supervision of the cognizant Officer in
   Charge, Marine Inspection.

7. The watertight door in the bulkhead at frame 18 shall be closed
   and properly dogged at all times when underway except when
   actually used for transit under safe conditions.

D037DG

8. Cross-connections between all tank sets shall be kept closed at all times when underway.

9. Bilges shall be kept pumped to minimum content at all times.

10. Jet fuel may be carried on deck in eight DOT tanks. The total weight of the fuel and tanks shall not exceed 23.16 long tons and the vertical center of gravity shall not exceed 3 feet 6 inches above the deck. Such tanks must be positively secured against shifting in a seaway prior to leaving protected waters. Neither passengers nor other deck cargo shall be carried when such tanks are aboard the vessel.

11. The Master should make every effort to determine the cause of any list of the vessel before taking corrective action.

It shall be the Master's responsibility to maintain the vessel in a satisfactory stability condition at all times.

This temporary stability letter shall be posted under suitable transparent material in the pilothouse of the vessel so that all pages are visible. It supersedes any stability information previously furnished the vessel.

Sincerely,

W. T. DOOR
Lieutenant Commander
U.S. Coast Guard

D037DG continued

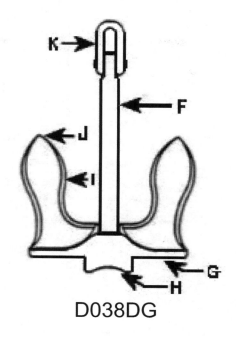

D038DG

D039DG

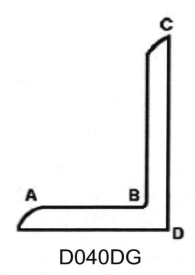

D040DG

D041DG

D042DG

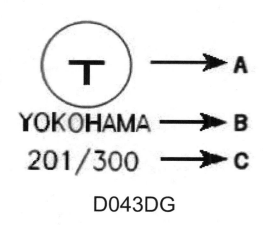

D043DG

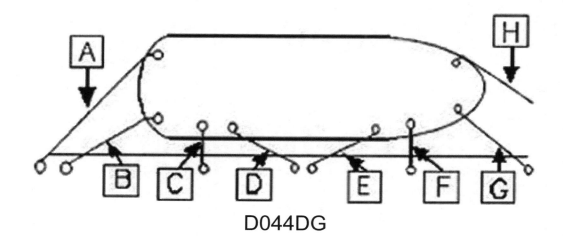

D044DG

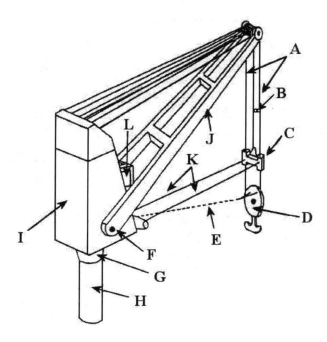

D045DG

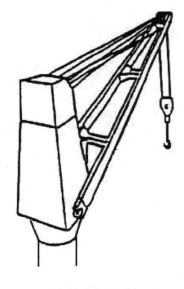

D046DG

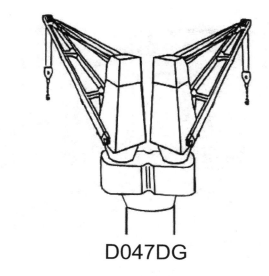

D047DG

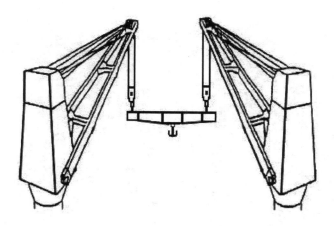

D048DG

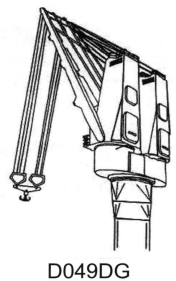

D049DG

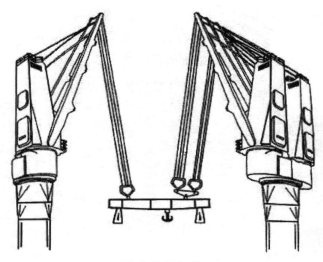

D050DG

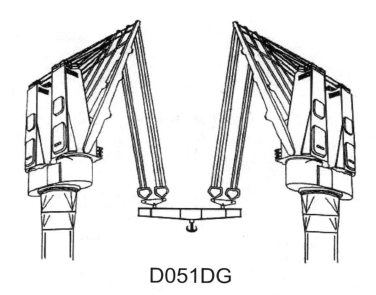

D051DG

D052DG THROUGH D057DG RESERVED

A.

B.

C.

D.

D058DG

CHAPTER 3
NAVIGATION GENERAL

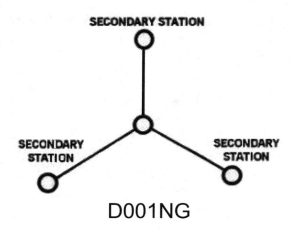

D001NG

D002NG: RESERVED

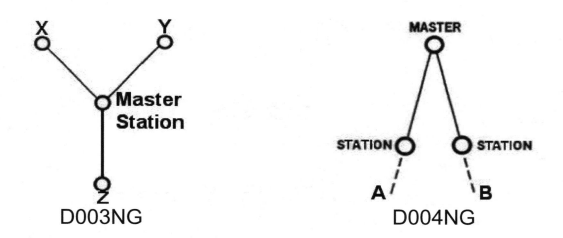

D003NG   D004NG

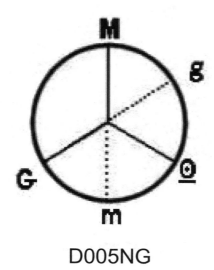

D005NG

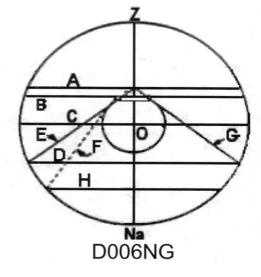

D006NG

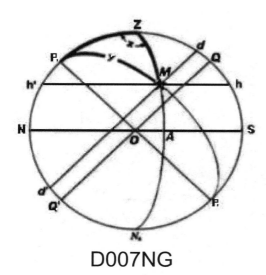

D007NG

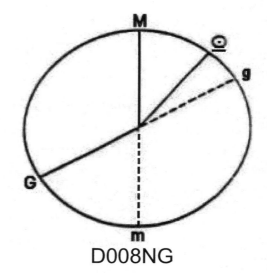

D008NG

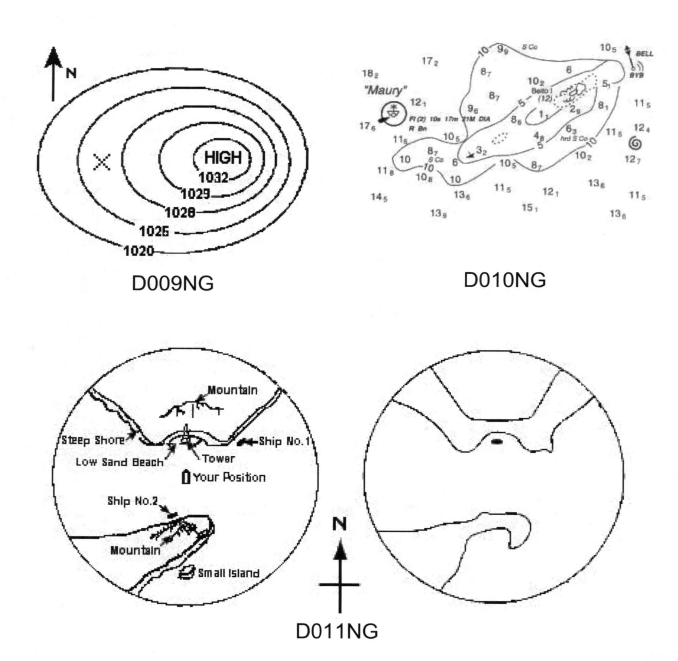

D009NG

D010NG

D011NG

D012NG: RESERVED

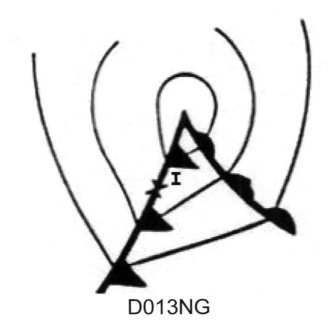

D013NG

D014NG

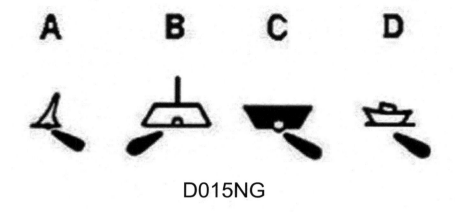

D015NG

D0016NG: RESERVED

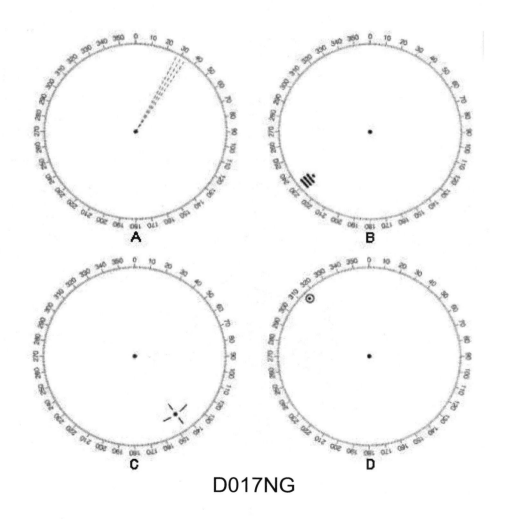

D017NG

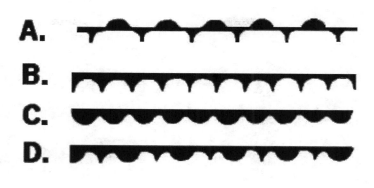

D018NG

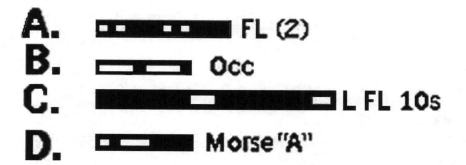

D019NG

D020NG   D021NG

D022NG

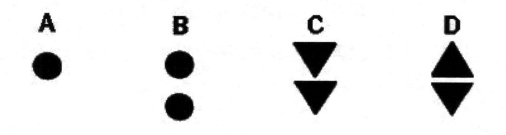

D023NG

D024NG

D025NG

D026NG

D027NG

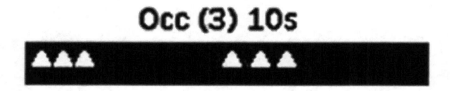

D028NG

D0029NG: RESERVED

D030NG

D031NG

A. ⚲ S   B. ⚲ BW   C. ⚲ RW   D. ⚲ RW

D032NG

RW
"A"

D033NG

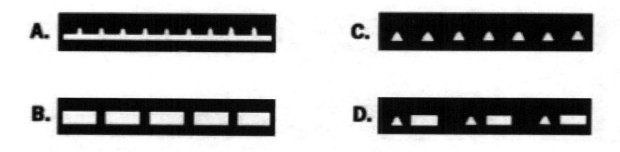

D034NG

DECODE FOR SURFACE ANALYSIS MESSAGES RECEIVED IN THE ABBREVIATED

INTERNATIONAL ANALYSIS CODE, IAC FLEET, FM 46

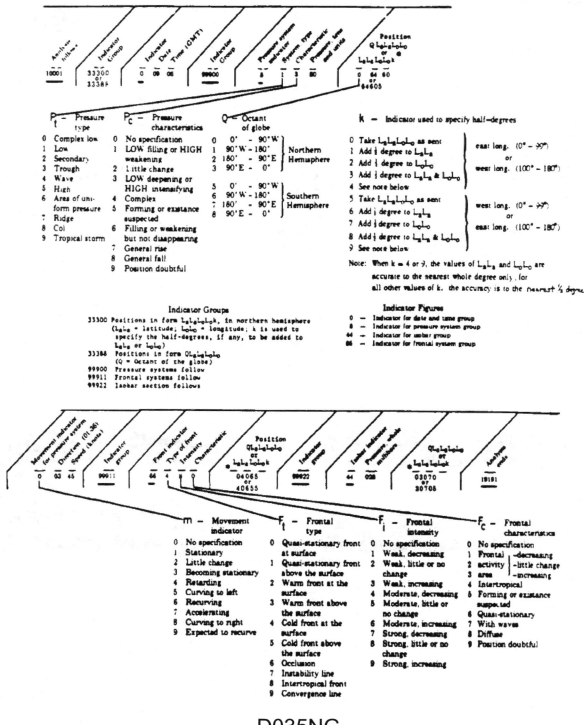

D035NG

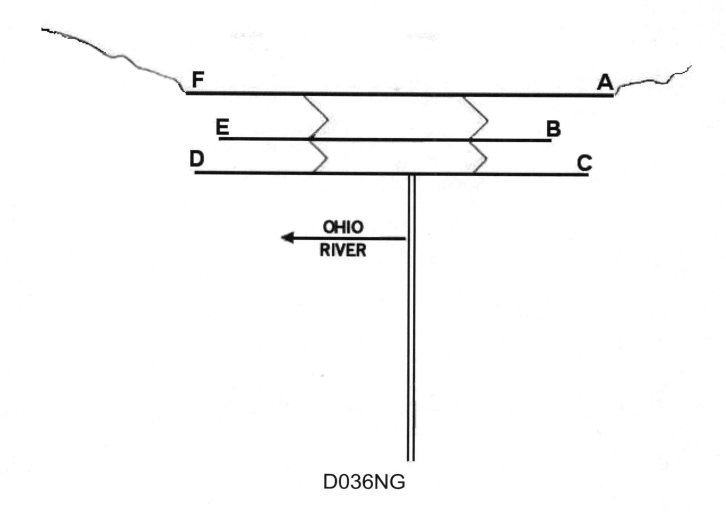

D036NG

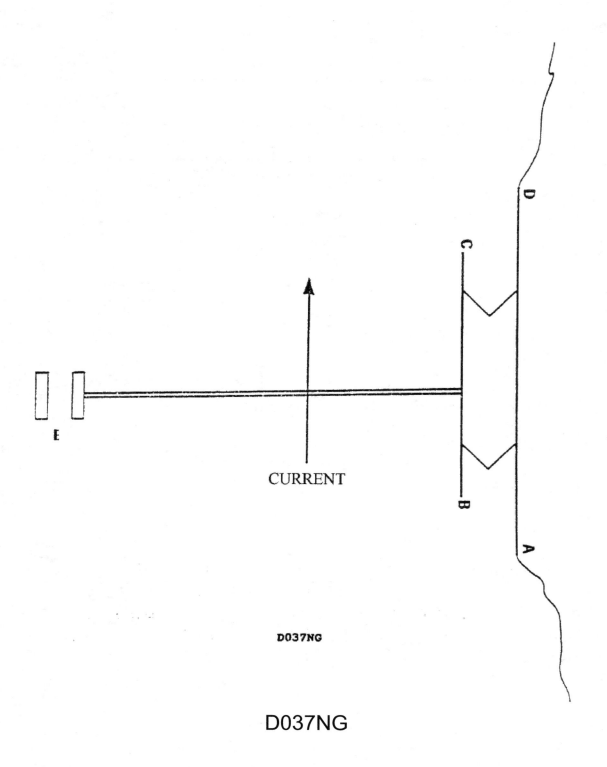

CURRENT

D037NG

D037NG

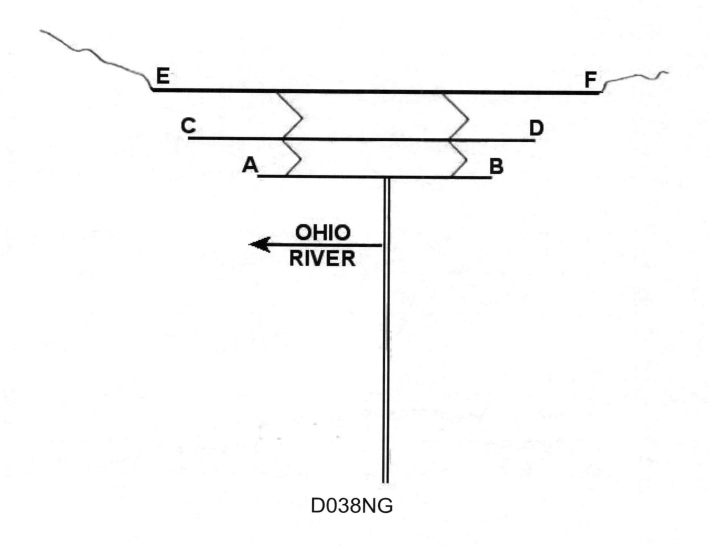

D038NG

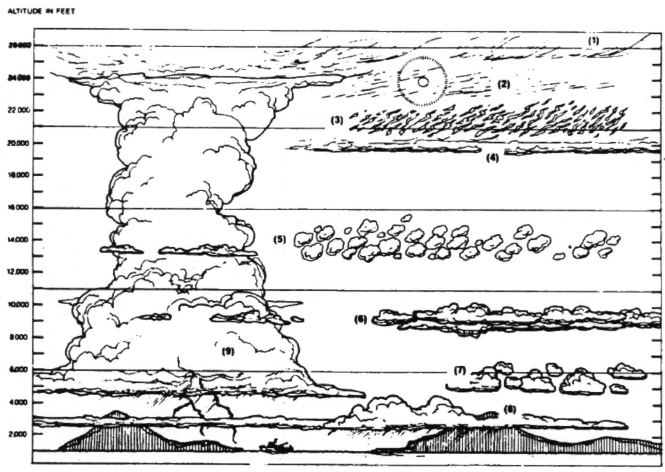

ALTITUDE IN FEET

Illustration courtesy NPFVAO SAFETY MANUAL. Produced in cooperation with
the National Fisheries Service and U.S. Coast Guard

D039NG

HEADING (GYRO)	VISUAL BEARING (GYRO)	RDF BEARING (GYRO)
061°	061°	062.5°
089°	059°	061.5°
114°	054°	057°
129°	039°	041°
144°	024°	025°
167.5°	017.5°	017°
197°	017°	016°
233.5°	023.5°	021.5°
271°	031°	027°
309°	039°	037.5°
336.5°	046.5°	046°
023.5°	053.5°	054°

D040NG

WS FORM B-80 (5-94) PRES. BY WMO DIRECTIVES					U.S. DEPARTMENT OF COMMERCE NATIONAL OCEANIC AND ATMOSPHERIC ADMINISTRATION NATIONAL WEATHER SERVICE

WEATHER REPORT FOR IMMEDIATE TRANSMISSION

NO.	SHIP NAME	DATE SENT (UTC)	TIME SENT (UTC)	STA. CALLED	FREQUENCY

ADDRESSES

U.S. Coast Guard: No address needed, start with BBXX indicator and ship's call sign.

INMARSAT

Standard A: Select—Coast Earth Station (CES), routine priority, duplex telex channel, and initiate call. When GA + is received, select 41 +. Upon receipt of answerback, NWS OBS MHTS, send the weather report starting with the BBXX indicator and ship's call sign. End the report with 5 periods. Try to limit INMARSAT call time to 30 seconds.

Standard C: To establish special access code 41, see manufacturers recommended instructions for set-up, or the Mariners Weather Log Summer, 1994, or later editions.

U.S. commercial and foreign radio stations: To: OBS METEO _____
(get address from "Radio Stations Accepting. . . . . "). Start with BBXX indicator and ship's call sign and combine the remaining numbers into 10-character groups.

INDICATOR	CALL SIGN	$YYGGi_w$	$99L_aL_aL_a$	$Q_cL_oL_oL_oL_o$	i_Ri_xhVV	Nddff
BBXX			**99**		**4**	
00fff	$1s_nTTT$	$2s_nT_dT_dT_d$	4PPPP	5appp	$7wwW_1W_2$	$8N_hC_LC_MC_H$
$222D_sv_s$	$0s_sT_wT_wT_w$	$2P_wP_wH_wH_w$	$3d_{w1}d_{w1}d_{w2}d_{w2}$	$4P_{w1}P_{w1}H_{w1}H_{w1}$	$5P_{w2}P_{w2}H_{w2}H_{w2}$	$6I_sE_sE_sR_s$
$8S_wT_bT_bT_b$	ICE	$c_iS_ib_iD_iz_i$	PLAIN LANGUAGE			TRANSMITTED BY

No Government Administration, or Company or person employed in the forwarding and delivery of this message shall be liable for any loss or damage arising from failure to transmit or to deliver the said message or from any neglect, delay, error or omission in the transmission thereof.

Supersedes NOAA Form 72-4A (1-82) which should be destroyed.

D041NG

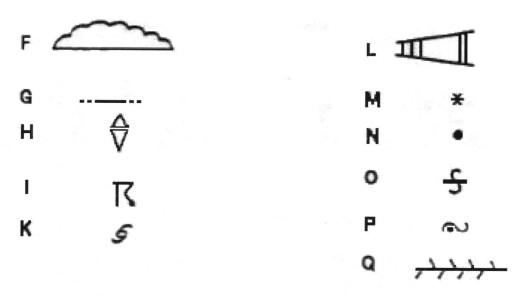

D042NG

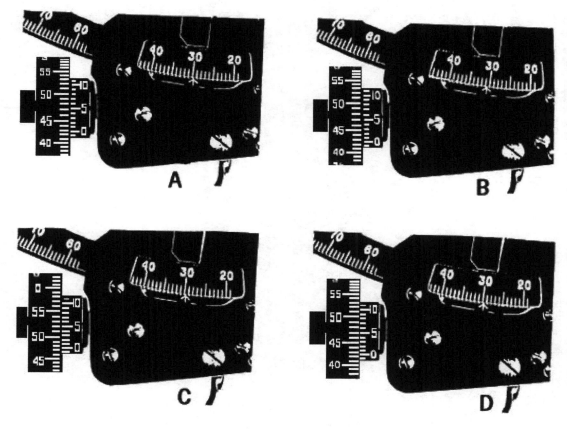

D043NG

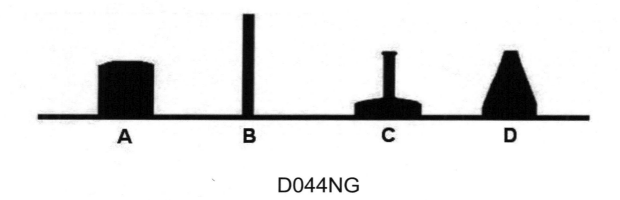

D044NG

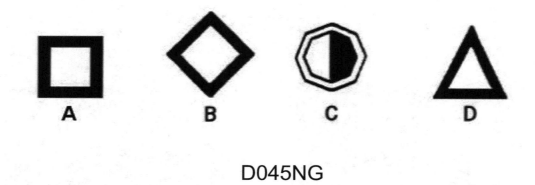

D045NG

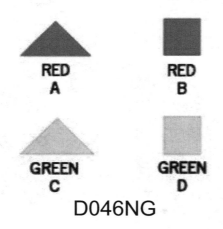

D046NG

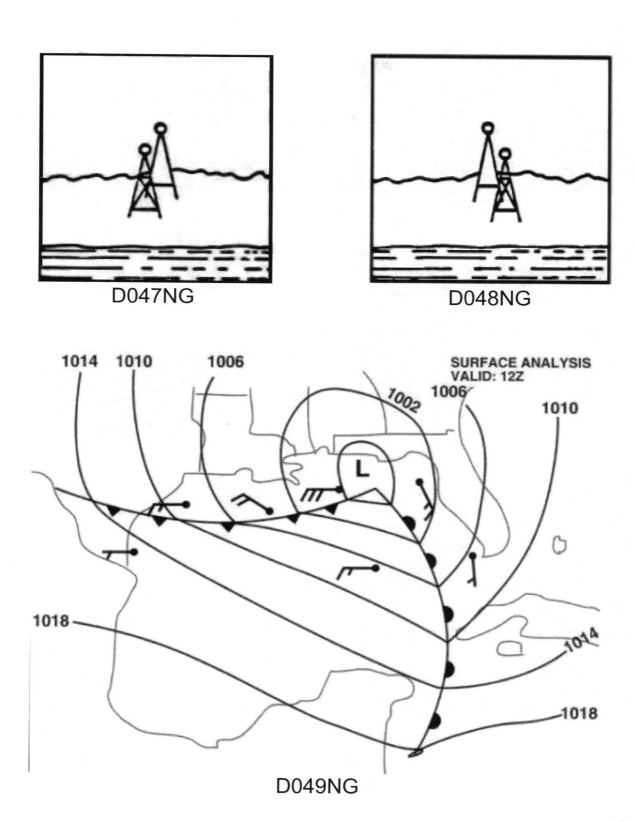

D047NG

D048NG

SURFACE ANALYSIS
VALID: 12Z

D049NG

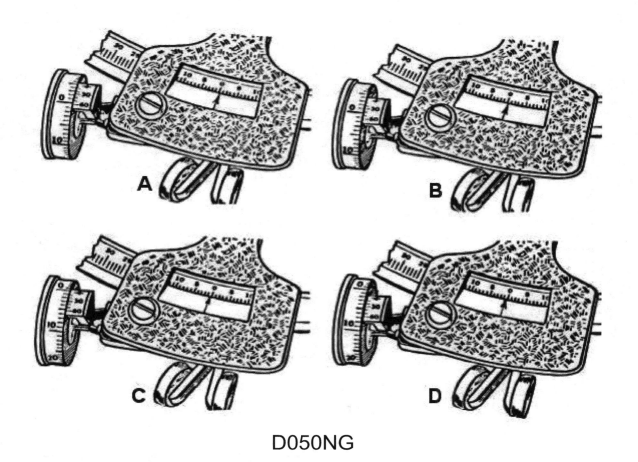

D050NG

D051NG

Fore-and-aft and athwartship magnets			Quadrantal spheres			Flinders bar		
Deviation → Magnets ↓	Easterly on east *and* westerly on west. (+B error)	Westerly on east *and* easterly on west. (-B error)	Deviation → Spheres ↓	E on NE, W on SE, E on SW, *and* W on NW (+D error)	W on NE, E on SE, W on SW, *and* E on NW (-D error)	Deviation change with latitude change → Bar ↓	E on E *and* W on W when sailing toward equator from north latitude or away from equator to south latitude.	W on E *and* E on W when sailing toward equator from north latitude or away from equator to south latitude.
No fore and aft magnets in binnacle.	Place magnets red forward.	Place magnets red aft.	No spheres on binnacle.	Place spheres athwartship.	Place spheres fore and aft.	No bar in holder.	Place required amount of bar forward.	Place required amount of bar aft.
Fore and aft magnets red forward.	Raise magnets.	Lower magnets.	Spheres at athwartship position.	Move spheres toward compass or use larger spheres.	Move spheres outwards or remove.	Bar forward of binnacle.	Increase amount of bar forward.	Decrease amount of bar forward.
Fore and aft magnets red aft.	Lower magnets.	Raise magnets.	Spheres at fore and aft position.	Move spheres outward or remove.	Move spheres toward compass or use larger spheres.	Bar aft of binnacle.	Decrease amount of bar aft.	Increase amount of bar aft.
Deviation → Magnets ↓	Easterly on north *and* westerly on south. (+C error)	Westerly on north *and* easterly on south. (-C error)	Deviation → Spheres ↓	E on N, W on E, E on S, *and* W on W (+E error)	W on N, E on E, W on S, *and* E on W (-E error)	↑ Bar Deviation change with latitude change →	W on E *and* E on W when sailing toward equator from south latitude or away from equator to north latitude.	E on E *and* W on W when sailing toward equator from south latitude or away from equator to north latitude.
No athwartship magnets in binnacle.	Place athwartship magnets red starboard.	Place athwartship magnets red port.	No spheres on binnacle.	Place spheres at port forward and starboard aft intercardinal points.	Place spheres at starboard forward and port aft intercardinal positions.	**Heeling magnet** (Adjust with changes in magnetic latitude)		
Athwartship magnets red starboard.	Raise magnets.	Lower magnets.	Spheres at athwartship position.	Slew spheres clockwise through required angle.	Slew spheres counter-clockwise through required angle.	If compass north is attracted to high side of ship when rolling, *raise* the heeling magnet if red end is up and *lower* the heeling magnet if blue end is up.		
Athwartship magnets red port.	Lower magnets.	Raise magnets.	Spheres at fore and aft position.	Slew spheres counter-clockwise through required angle.	Slew spheres clockwise through required angle.	If compass north is attracted to low side of ship when rolling, *lower* the heeling magnet if red end is up and *raise* the heeling magnet if blue end is up. NOTE: Any change in placement of the heeling magnet will affect the deviation on all headings.		

D052NG

CHAPTER 4
SAFETY & ENVIRONMENTAL PROTECTION

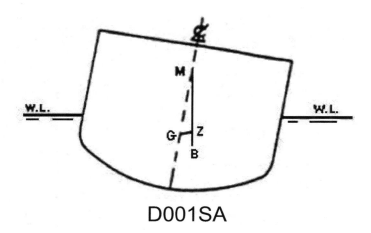

D001SA

D002SA AND D003SA: RESERVED

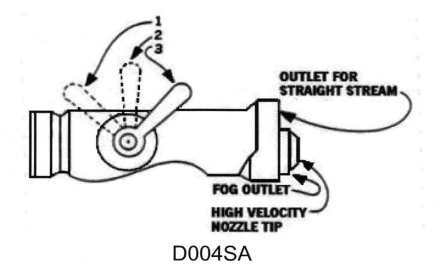

D004SA

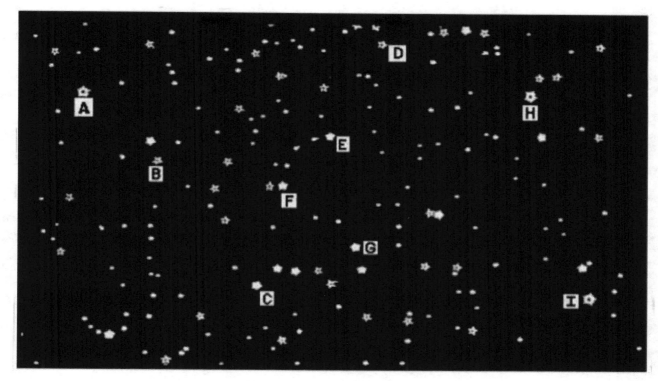

D005SA

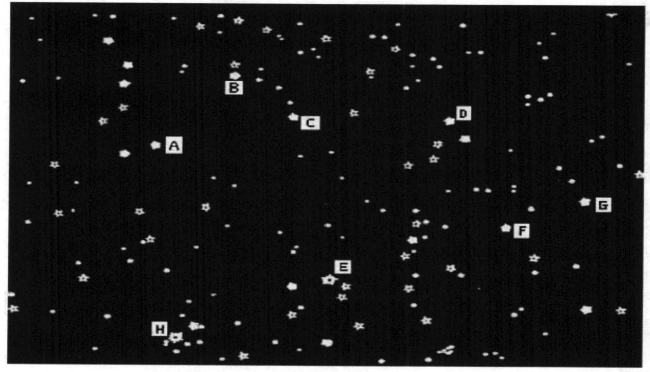

D006SA

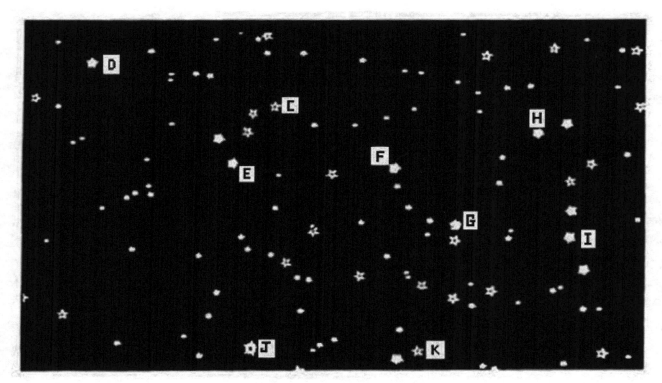

D007SA

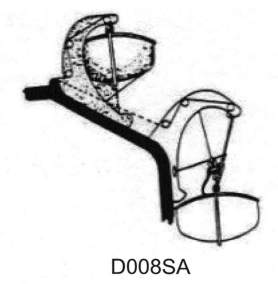

D008SA

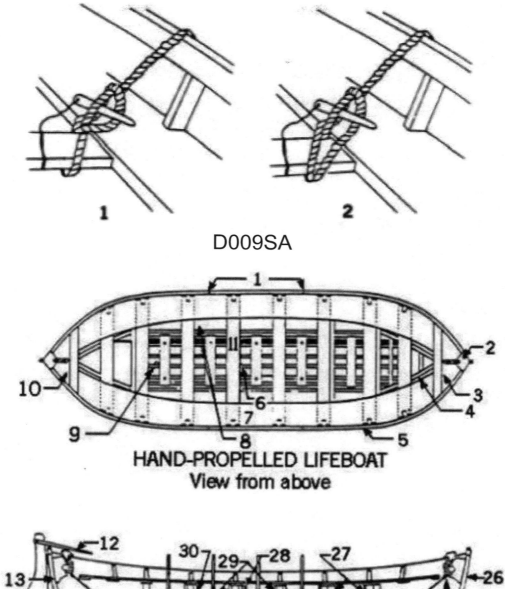

D009SA

HAND-PROPELLED LIFEBOAT
View from above

HAND-PROPELLED LIFEBOAT
Profile View

D010SA

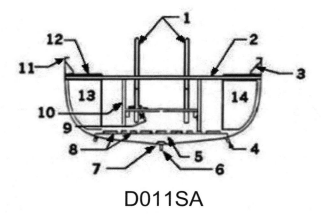

D011SA

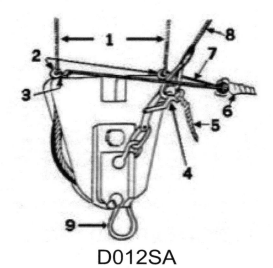

D012SA

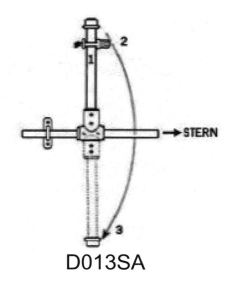

D013SA

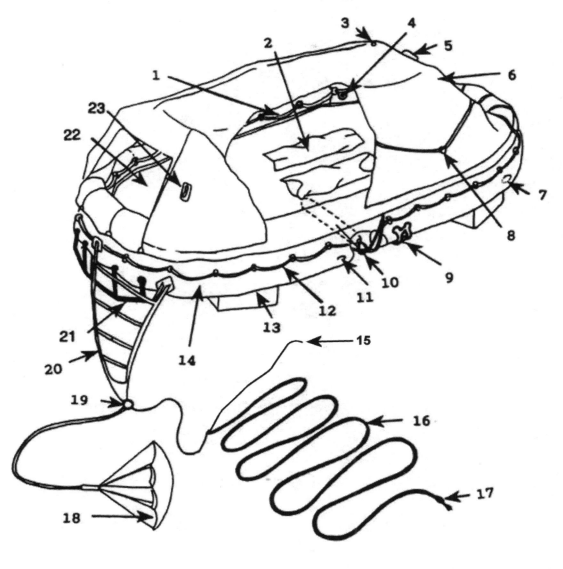

D014SA

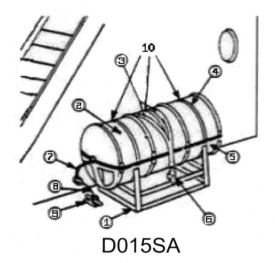

D015SA

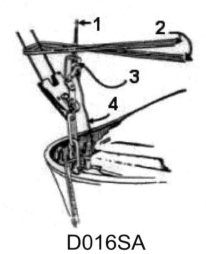

D016SA

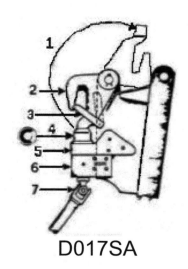

D017SA

D018SA AND D034SA: RESERVED

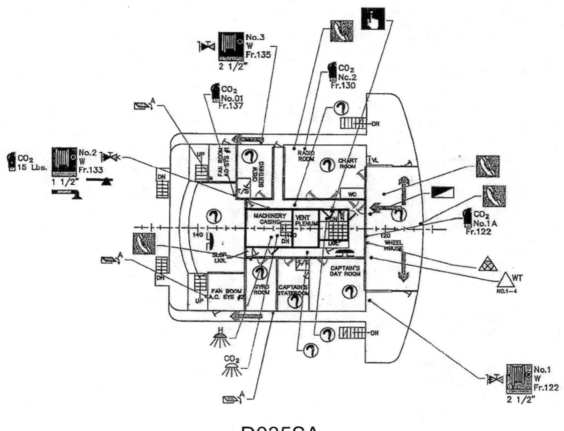

D035SA

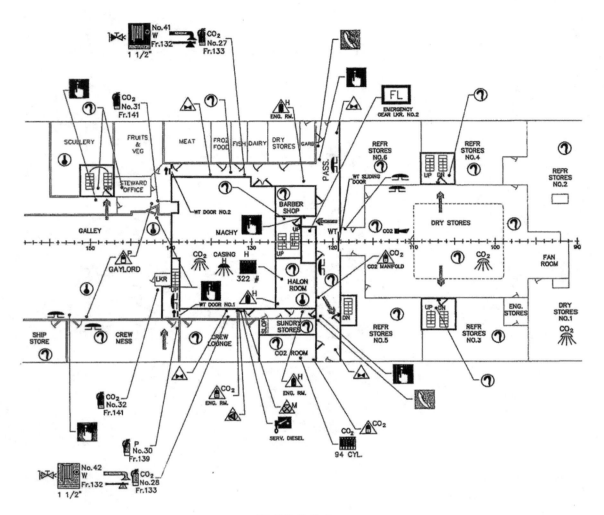

D036SA

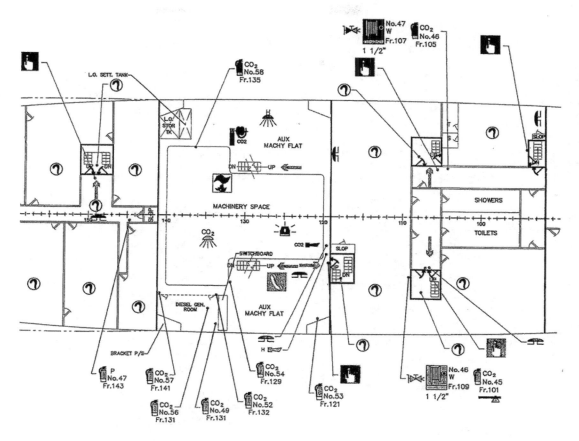

D037SA

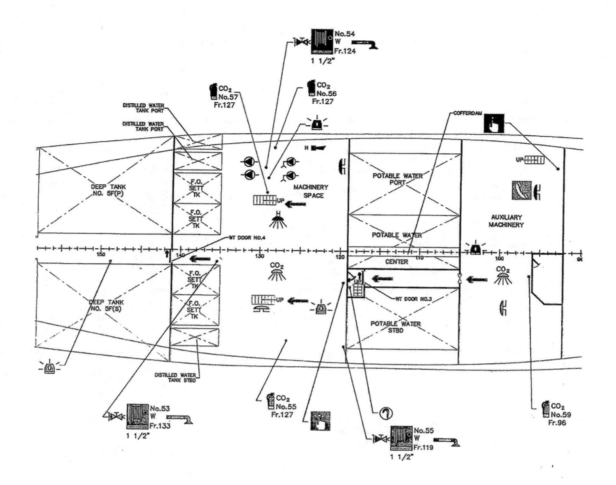

D038SA

IMO Fire Control Symbols

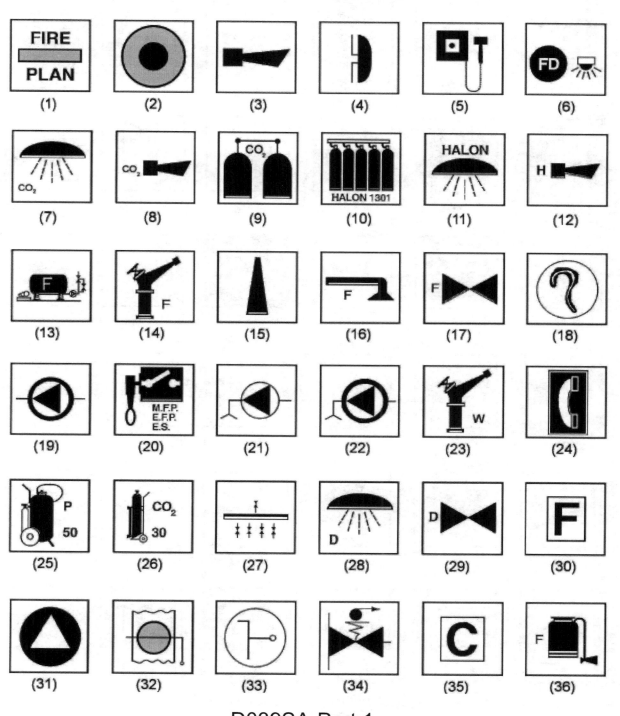

D039SA-Part 1

IMO Fire Control Symbols

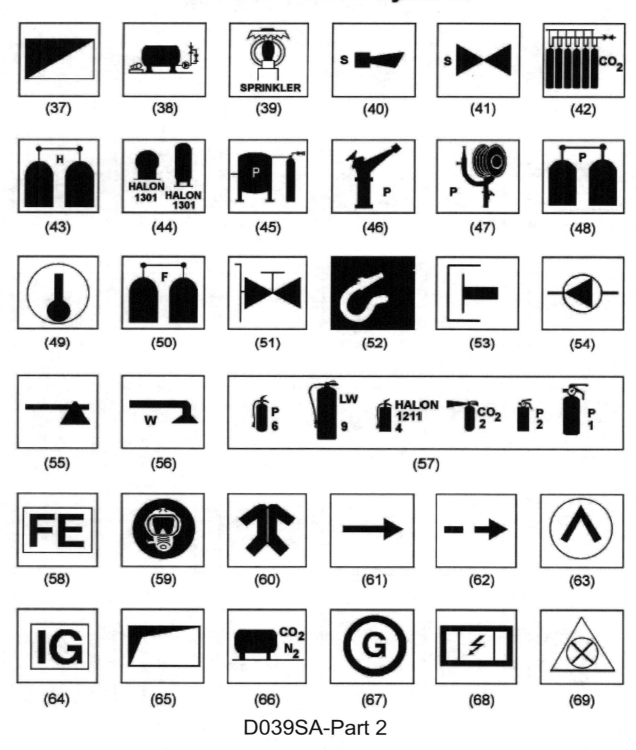

D039SA-Part 2

CHAPTER 5
SAIL

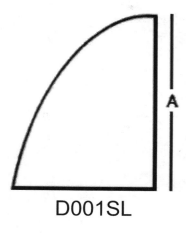

D001SL

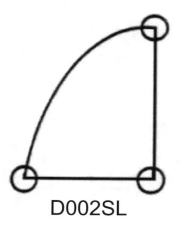

D002SL

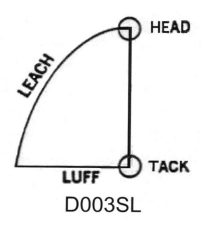

D003SL